The Alex
OMNIBUS

Other cartoon books by the same author

Alex (Mandarin)

with Mark Warren
Celeb (Corgi)

The Alex
OMNIBUS

PENGUIN BOOKS

Published by the Penguin Group
Penguin Books Ltd, 27 Wrights Lane, London W8 5TZ, England
Penguin Books USA Inc., 375 Hudson Street, New York, New York 10014, USA
Penguin Books Australia Ltd, Ringwood, Victoria, Australia
Penguin Books Canada Ltd, 10 Alcorn Avenue, Toronto, Ontario, Canada M4V 3B2
Penguin Books (NZ) Ltd, 182–190 Wairau Road, Auckland 10, New Zealand

Penguin Books Ltd, Registered Offices: Harmondsworth, Middlesex, England

These cartoon strips first appeared in the *Independent*
The Unabashed Alex first published in Penguin Books 1988
Alex II: Magnum Force first published in Penguin Books 1989
Alex III: Son of Alex first published in Penguin Books 1990
Alex IV: The Man with the Golden Handshake first published in Penguin Books 1991
This omnibus edition, *Alex: The Independent Years*, first published 1992
10 9 8 7 6 5 3 2 1

Copyright © Peattie and Taylor, 1988, 1989, 1990, 1991
All rights reserved

Additional material by Mark Warren

The moral right of the authors has been asserted

Printed in England by Clays Ltd, St Ives plc

Alex

Penny
(Alex's wife)

Clive

Bridget
(Clive's girlfriend.)

Rupert
(Alex's boss.)

Ruth
(American trader.)

Greg.
(Alex's brother,
a journalist.)

Vince
(a money broker)

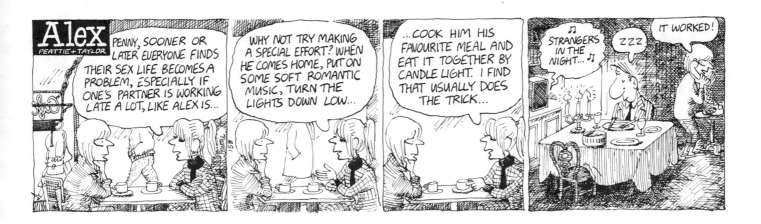

THE CRASH OF '87...

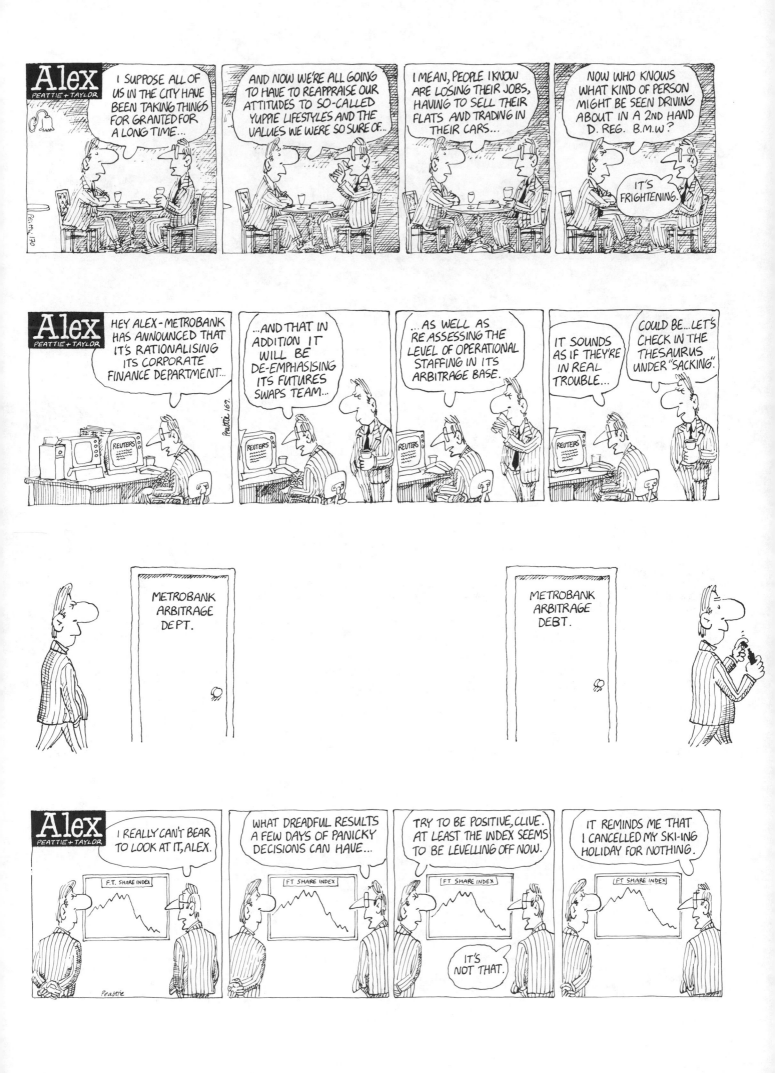

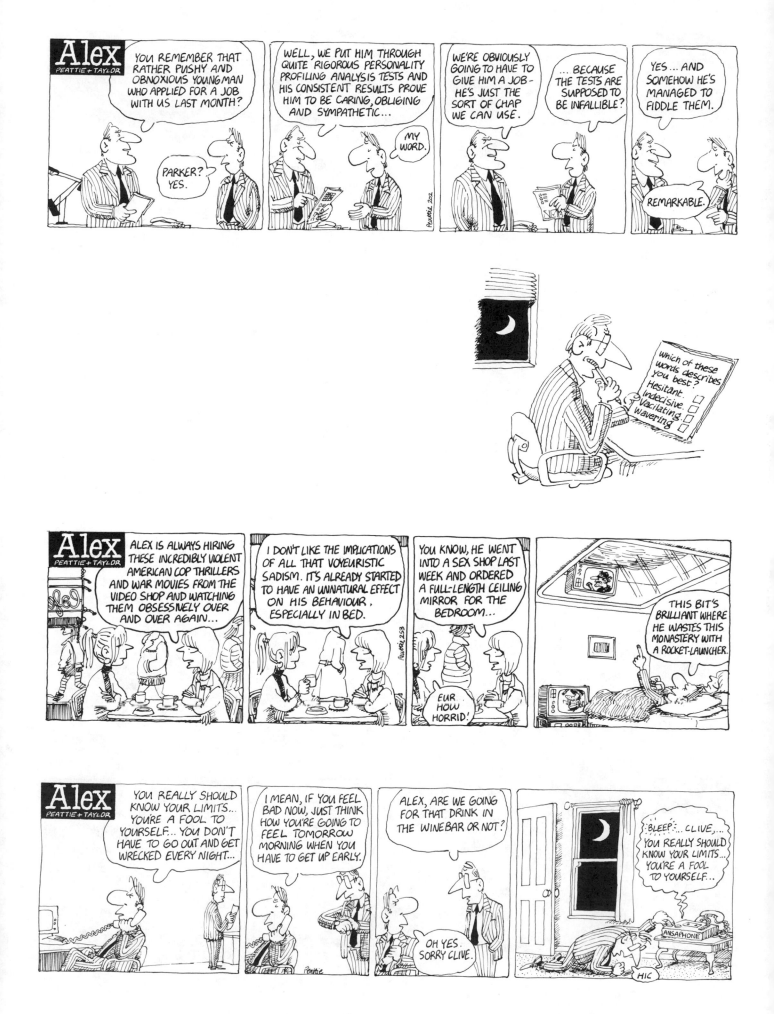

PASS THE PORTABLE TELEPHONE.

Alex PEATTIE + TAYLOR

I'M GOING TO HAVE TO GO TO A BIT OF EXTRA TROUBLE WITH MY THANKYOU LETTER TO MY AUNT ALICE THIS YEAR, CAROLINE.

FOR MY BIRTHDAY INSTEAD OF THE USUAL CHEAP SET OF HANKIES, I GOT A NOT INEXPENSIVE SILK SCARF...READY?

YES.

"DEAR AUNT ALICE, THANKS FOR THE PRESENT. YOUR NEPHEW ALEX"

SHALL I "RED STAR" THIS UP TO PETERBOROUGH AS USUAL?

TAP TAP TAP

...ER NO. BETTER HAVE IT HAND-DELIVERED BY TAXI THIS YEAR, PLEASE, CAROLINE.

IT REALLY IS A CHALLENGE TO YOU TO SPEND MORE ON THE THANKYOU LETTER THAN SHE DOES ON THE PRESENT ISN'T IT, ALEX?

Alex PEATTIE + TAYLOR

YOU SAY YOU ACTUALLY HAVE FILM OF THE INTRUDER, SIR?

YES OFFICER.

WITH A MINI SECURITY VIDEO CAMERA HIDDEN INSIDE A FALSE BOOK ON THE BOOKSHELF...

CLICK

THAT'S HIM IS IT, SIR?

YES OFFICER. AS YOU SEE HE HELPED HIMSELF TO QUITE A FEW THINGS...I'VE MADE A FULL LIST...

AVOCADO DIP... TWO PIECES OF QUICHE...

AND HAVE YOU HAD PROBLEMS WITH GATECRASHERS AT PREVIOUS PARTIES, SIR?

Alex PEATTIE + TAYLOR

THAT OLD FRIEND YOU MET AT THE PARTY, WAS SHE REALLY ONCE "PLAYMATE OF THE MONTH" IN SOME PORN MAG?

OH... YES...

IT WAS VERY STUPID OF YOU TO MAKE MENTION OF IT IN FRONT OF ALL THOSE PEOPLE. IT WAS BOUND TO CAUSE EMBARRASSMENT...

I KNOW, I DIDN'T THINK...

THOUGH I MUST SAY I WAS SURPRISED TO HEAR ALL THOSE FEEBLE CLICHÉD JUSTIFICATIONS: "I WAS VERY YOUNG AT THE TIME; I DIDN'T REALLY KNOW WHAT I WAS DOING; I THOUGHT IT WOULD BE ARTISTIC; IT WAS JUST TOO TEMPTING..."

SORRY BRIDGET, I WAS JUST GABBLING HYSTERICALLY...

...AND WHEN YOU CLAIMED THE MAG HAD BEEN DELIVERED BY MISTAKE INSTEAD OF "HOME COMPUTER WEEKLY"...

Alex PEATTIE + TAYLOR

I HEAR THE POLICE HAVE LAUNCHED INVESTIGATIONS INTO IRREGULARITIES DURING THE BROMEX TAKEOVER.

YES. ONE OR TWO TOP CHAPS UNDER SUSPICION APPARENTLY.

...IT EVEN LOOKS AS IF OLD BUFFY FROBISHER HAS FOUND HIMSELF IN A SPOT OF BOTHER WITH THE AUTHORITIES.

MY WORD.

YES. FIRST THING HIS WIFE KNEW ABOUT IT WAS WHEN A COUPLE OF P.C.s ARRIVED AT HER FRONT DOOR ONE MORNING...

POLICE CONSTABLES FROM SCOTLAND YARD?

NO. POST CARDS FROM BOLIVIA.

Alex PEATTIE + TAYLOR

IF IT WASN'T EMBARRASSING ENOUGH HAVING STARTED TO COME TO CHURCH ON SUNDAYS JUST BECAUSE WE'RE GETTING MARRIED HERE..

...I'M SURE THE VICAR CAN'T FAIL TO HAVE NOTICED THE SWELLING AROUND MY MIDDLE...

WELL, YOU'RE THE ONE WHO INSISTS ON BEING SO SECRETIVE, PENNY

I'M PREPARED TO BE QUITE OPEN ABOUT IT. THE CHURCH IS QUITE LIBERAL THESE DAYS. IT ACCEPTS THAT OUR GENERATION HAS DIFFERENT CUSTOMS.

PASS ME THE 'LIFESTYLE' SUPPLEMENT WILL YOU, PENNY.

SHHH. NOT SO LOUD.

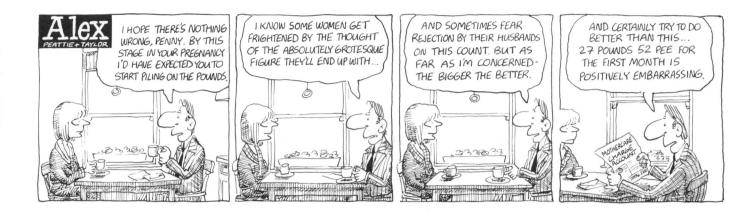

Alex PEATTIE + TAYLOR

I HOPE THERE'S NOTHING WRONG, PENNY. BY THIS STAGE IN YOUR PREGNANCY I'D HAVE EXPECTED YOU TO START PILING ON THE POUNDS.

I KNOW SOME WOMEN GET FRIGHTENED BY THE THOUGHT OF THE ABSOLUTELY GROTESQUE FIGURE THEY'LL END UP WITH...

AND SOMETIMES FEAR REJECTION BY THEIR HUSBANDS ON THIS COUNT. BUT AS FAR AS I'M CONCERNED - THE BIGGER THE BETTER.

AND CERTAINLY TRY TO DO BETTER THAN THIS... 27 POUNDS 52 PEE FOR THE FIRST MONTH IS POSITIVELY EMBARRASSING.

Alex PEATTIE + TAYLOR

I'M ONLY SIX WEEKS PREGNANT, CHLOE. ISN'T IT A BIT EARLY TO BE DOING THESE EXERCISES?

IT'S NEVER TOO EARLY TO GET YOUR BODY IN SHAPE FOR THE TASK IT WILL HAVE TO PERFORM, PENNY.

BRACE YOURSELF ON YOUR BACK... BREATHE DEEPLY AND EASILY... NOW PUSH... CONTRACT THOSE TUMMY MUSCLES... PUSH AS HARD AS YOU CAN... GOOD...

NNNGH...

HOW LONG WILL IT LAST?

A COUPLE OF MONTHS...

...UNTIL YOU REALLY CAN'T SQUEEZE INTO JEANS ANYMORE, THEN I'M AFRAID YOU'LL JUST HAVE TO START WEARING MATERNITY DRESSES.

Alex PEATTIE + TAYLOR

WHO IS THIS MINIATURE TOY VACUUM CLEANER FOR?

IT'S FOR TIM AND LYDIA'S LITTLE GIRL ANTONIA.

OH DEAR... I'M NOT SURE HOW HAPPY TIM AND LYDIA WILL BE ABOUT THEIR LITTLE GIRL BEING GIVEN A PRESENT SEEMINGLY DESIGNED TO INITIATE HER INTO THE RITUALS OF FEMALE DOMESTIC SERVITUDE.

OH... I SEE WHAT YOU MEAN... YOU THINK THEY WANT HER TO GROW UP LIBERATED FROM SEXUAL STEREOTYPING?

WELL IT'S A POSSIBILITY...

BUT I THINK THEY'RE CERTAINLY TAKING IT FOR GRANTED THAT SHE'LL HAVE A CLEANING LADY.

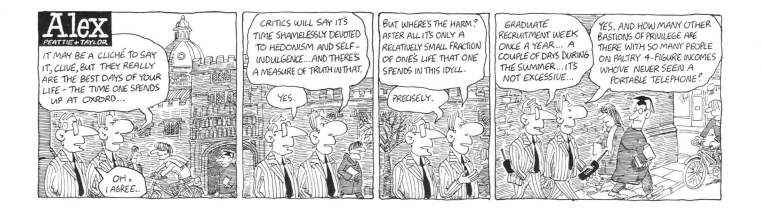

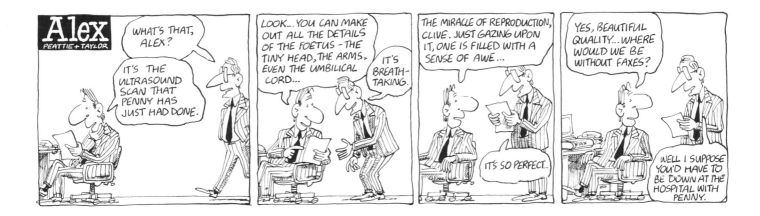

BANK GOLF DAY

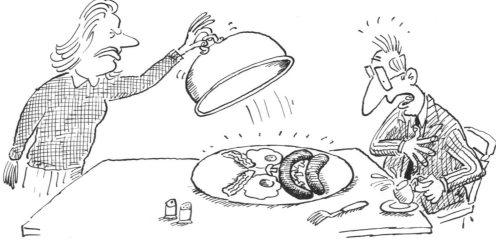

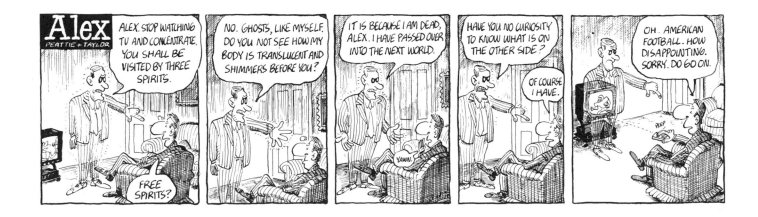

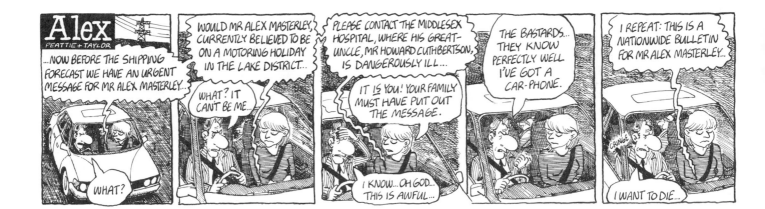

Alex PEATTIE + TAYLOR

MAYBE WE MADE THE WRONG DECISION, ALEX... THOSE WEEKS THAT GREAT UNCLE HOWARD WAS IN HOSPITAL WERE A PRETTY GHASTLY TIME.

LET'S FACE IT...WE KNEW HE WAS GOING TO DIE... I KNOW WE DISCUSSED THE QUESTION OF SWITCHING OFF THE MACHINE.

IT SEEMED WRONG SOMEHOW... BUT MAYBE IT WOULD HAVE BEEN BETTER THAT WAY... THE NEXT OF KIN HAVE A LOT OF DIFFICULT RESPONSIBILITIES.

EXACTLY. AND I DON'T SEE WHY TRANSCRIBING THE DECEASED'S ANSAFONE MESSAGES SHOULD BE ONE OF THEM. I'LL GET MY SECRETARY TO DO IT.

...HELLO HOWARD IT'S DAVID MASON AGAIN...

Alex PEATTIE + TAYLOR

THERE WAS ONE EMBARRASSING MOMENT WHEN MY COUSIN BROUGHT THE URN CONTAINING MY UNCLE'S REMAINS INTO THE HOUSE.

HE ONLY TRIPPED UP AND SPILLED THE ASHES ALL OVER THE CARPET. OH NO.

YES. IT CAUSED CONSIDERABLE DISTRESS TO SOME OF MY ELDERLY RELATIVES. I SUPPOSE IT BROUGHT HOME THE FACT THAT YOUR UNCLE WAS NO MORE.

NO. IT REMINDED THEM THAT HE STARTED HIS CAREER AS A DOOR-TO-DOOR SALESMAN DEMONSTRATING VACUUM CLEANERS. HOW DREADFUL.

R.I.P.

R.P.I.

Alex PEATTIE + TAYLOR

WHAT'S THAT BROCHURE, ALEX? CRYOGENIC POST-DEATH FREEZING TECHNIQUES, CLIVE. A CHANCE TO LIVE AGAIN IN THE FUTURE.

WELL I MUST SAY THAT RAISES SOME DIFFICULT QUESTIONS ABOUT MORALITY WHEN WE'RE IGNORING THE POVERTY AND SUFFERING OF THOSE AROUND US.

SHOULDN'T WE DO MORE TO HELP OTHERS HERE AND NOW? PLUS, WHAT HAPPENS TO THE SOUL IF THERE'S AN AFTER LIFE? VERY TRUE.

AND THIS WAY YOU GET A CHANCE TO COME BACK AND BE GOOD IF THERE IS ONE, OR ELSE TO RETURN AND BE A TOTAL BASTARD WITHOUT WORRYING. BRILLIANT! HOW MUCH DOES IT COST?

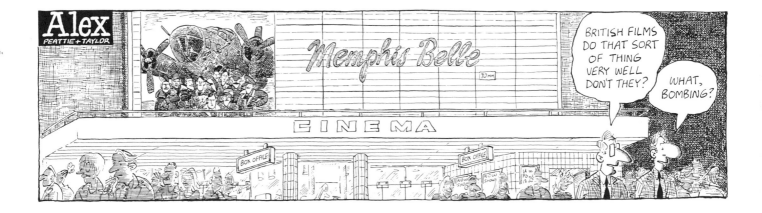

Strip 1:

OH DEAR. POOR OLD CLIVE, LOOK AT THAT.

OH IT'S ALL IN A GOOD CAUSE, PENNY.

IN THESE CHARITY AUCTIONS IT'S ALWAYS THE PEOPLE WHO'VE HAD MOST TO DRINK WHO ARE THE PEOPLE WHO END UP PAYING A LOT OF MONEY FOR THE ITEMS UNDER THE HAMMER.

WHICH EXPLAINS THE ALL TOO FORESEEABLE PREDICAMENT THAT CLIVE HAS ENDED UP IN.

STILL SOBER.

YES. HE HASN'T MANAGED TO ATTRACT THE ATTENTION OF THE WINE WAITER OR THE AUCTIONEER ALL EVENING.

AHEM...

ANY MORE BIDS?

Strip 2:

OBVIOUSLY THIS BALL CAN'T POSSIBLY HOPE TO RAISE AS MUCH MONEY FOR CHARITY AS PREVIOUS YEARS' EVENTS HAVE DONE.

NO.

WITH THE ECONOMIC RECESSION AND THE NEW MOOD OF AUSTERITY INEVITABLY GUESTS CAN NO LONGER AFFORD THE LAVISH EXPENDITURE OF TIMES GONE BY.

IT'S SAD OF COURSE, BUT ONE DOES DETECT CERTAIN CHANGES.

YES, I'D NOTICED...

THE FOOD AND WINE ARE DEFINITELY OF A MUCH HIGHER STANDARD THAN LAST YEAR.

CLEARLY PEOPLE NEED TO FEEL THE TICKET PRICE REPRESENTS BETTER VALUE FOR MONEY THESE DAYS.

Strip 3:

FRANKLY, CLIVE, US CHARITY WORKERS GET SICK OF LISTENING TO CONDESCENDING EXPRESSIONS OF SYMPATHY FOR THE PEOPLE THESE EVENTS ARE ABOUT.

OH.

YOU'RE SO TYPICAL. YOU NEVER HAVE TO MEET THEM. IT'S EASY FOR YOU TO CLAIM YOU FEEL PITY FOR THEM AND SYMPATHISE WITH THE DREADFUL CONDITIONS THEY HAVE TO LIVE WITH.

BUT IT'S TRUE. I DO FEEL SORRY FOR THEM.

THAT'S A PATRONISING ATTITUDE WHICH IS TOTALLY INSINCERE. WHEN IT COMES TO THE CRUNCH YOUR SORT ALWAYS FAILS TO TRANSLATE WHAT YOU PROFESS INTO WHAT YOU ACTUALLY DO.

YES. I ADMIT IT. YOU'RE RIGHT...

...I'D PROBABLY CRINGE AND GROVEL AND UTTERLY LOSE MY DIGNITY...

QUITE. INTERFACING WITH ROYAL PERSONAGES TAKES PRACTICE.

Strip 4:

I'VE BEEN A CHARITY COLLECTOR FOR YEARS BUT IT'S ALWAYS A REALLY SPECIAL EXPERIENCE TO WORK WITH THE ROYALS.

OBVIOUSLY THEY INSTINCTIVELY RESPOND TO AN APPEAL FOR CHARITY LIKE ANY OTHER OF US...

BUT THE THING ABOUT THEM IS THEY HAVE THIS AIR OF SERENITY AND SINCERITY ABOUT THEM WHICH MEMBERS OF THE GENERAL PUBLIC LACK.

WHEN MAKING LAME PROTESTATIONS ABOUT HAVING NO MONEY ON THEM?

EXACTLY IN THE ROYALS' CASE IT'S ACTUALLY TRUE.

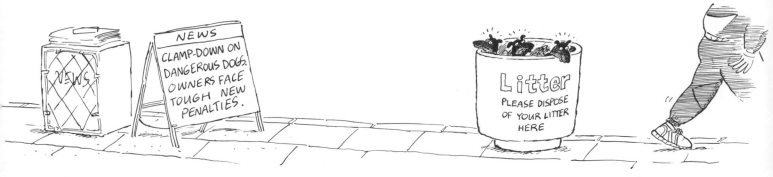

PASSPORT
UNITED KINGDOM OF
GREAT BRITAIN AND
NORTHERN IRELAND

Name. *Mr John Biggs*

Occupation. *Photographer*
(The Independent)

Date of birth *1st Aug 58*

Place of birth *LONDON*

Height *5'10"*

Bearer

PHOTO

Alex PEATTIE + TAYLOR

WELL, WELL. LOOK WHO'S OVER THERE.

HEAVENS! IT'S TOBY CARRINGTON AND JULIAN GROVES.

EXACTLY. HEADS OF TWO OF THE DEADLIEST OF RIVAL COMPANIES IN THE CITY, AND THEY HATE EACH OTHER'S GUTS BY ALL ACCOUNTS.

YET HERE THEY ARE SITTING NEXT TO EACH OTHER.

IT SAYS A LOT ABOUT THEIR SPIRIT OF CHARITY ON THIS JOYOUS OCCASION OF GIVING...

IT CERTAINLY DOES.

EACH OF THEM WAS OBVIOUSLY TOO MEAN TO COUGH UP FOR A WHOLE TABLE.

CHEAPSKATES. SERVES THEM RIGHT.

Alex PEATTIE + TAYLOR

THESE CHARITY BALLS ARE SO DIFFERENT FROM THE NORMAL ROUND OF SOCIAL DINNERS AND EVENTS.

OH, VERY MUCH SO. ON THOSE OTHER OCCASIONS ONE ONLY EVER MIXES WITH PEOPLE WHO ARE TOTALLY ENSCONCED IN THE MORES AND VALUES OF SOCIETY LIVING.

WHEREAS HERE ONE IS IN THE COMPANY OF PEOPLE WHO DON'T JUST TURN A DELIBERATE BLIND EYE TO THOSE LESS PRIVILEGED THAN THEMSELVES.

LIKE CLIVE, FOR EXAMPLE...

EXACTLY... LOOK AT HIM TALKING TO THE SERVING STAFF.

FRANKLY IT'S EMBARRASSING TO BE SEATED NEXT TO HIM.

THANK YOU VERY MUCH INDEED...

Alex PEATTIE + TAYLOR

WELL IT'S CERTAINLY PROVED A SUCCESS HAVING YOU PROFESSIONALS COME IN AND RUN A ROULETTE TABLE FOR US.

IT'S GOING VERY NICELY SIR, YES.

IT'S ALWAYS INTERESTING TO ME SEEING HOW PEOPLE'S DEMEANOUR AND MOOD SEEMS TO LOOSEN UP AS SOON AS WE OPEN THE TABLES.

AND IT ALL HELPS RAISE MONEY FOR CHARITY.

YES. I DON'T KNOW WHY BUT THERE'S SOMETHING ABOUT HAVING A CASINO AT A CHARITY BALL THAT GETS GUESTS TO PUT THEIR HANDS IN THEIR POCKETS.

ER... WELL IT'S NOT WANTING TO BE MISTAKEN FOR ONE OF YOU CROUPIERS ACTUALLY, SINCE YOU INVARIABLY HAVE YOUR ONES SEWN UP.

YES. THAT'S WHY I DO IT.

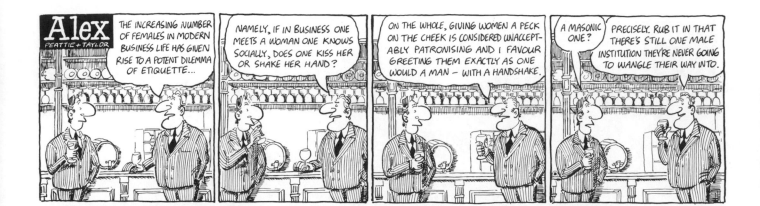

Alex
PEATTIE + TAYLOR

Panel 1: IT'S SO DEPRESSING TO COME HOME AND FIND YOU'VE BEEN BURGLED.

THANK GOODNESS WE WERE FULLY INSURED.

Panel 2: THOUGH OBVIOUSLY NO AMOUNT OF MONEY CAN COMPENSATE FOR THE HEARTACHE CAUSED BY THE THEFT OF CERTAIN ITEMS.

Panel 3: AFTER ALL THERE ARE SOME THINGS WHICH JUST CAN'T BE REPLACED...

Panel 4: OH NONSENSE. EXPLAIN TO THE MAN IN THE SHOP THAT YOU'VE HAD ONE FOR YEARS BUT IT JUST GOT STOLEN.

PENNY, I CANNOT BRING MYSELF TO BUY A C.D. PLAYER.

Alex
PEATTIE + TAYLOR

Panel 1: SO HOW DOES IT FEEL BEING BACK AT YOUR DESK AFTER SIX WEEKS OFF TO HAVE A BABY?

IT'S BEEN A TERRIBLE WRENCH, RUTH.

Panel 2: YOU CAN'T IMAGINE THAT ACUTE SENSE OF LOSS WHEN YOU FIND YOURSELF SUDDENLY SEPARATED FROM A HUMAN BEING WHOSE NEEDS YOU'VE BECOME ACCUSTOMED TO TENDING TO...

Panel 3: A RELATIONSHIP YOU'VE BUILT UP THROUGH CARE AND LOVING DEVOTION HAS BEEN RUPTURED AND YOU WONDER IF IT CAN EVER BE REPAIRED...IT'S VERY UPSETTING

Panel 4: HEY, DON'T LOOK AT ME. I WASN'T THE ONE WHO PINCHED YOUR BEST CLIENT WHILE YOU WERE ON MATERNITY LEAVE.

IT'S ALL THAT BLOODY BABY'S FAULT...

Alex
PEATTIE + TAYLOR

Panel 1: I REMEMBER THE OUTCRY A FEW YEARS BACK WHEN BRITISH AIRWAYS REDESIGNED ITS WHOLE CORPORATE IDENTITY.

Panel 2: REGULAR TRAVELLERS LIKE YOU AND I CONSIDERED IT A POINTLESS WASTE OF SEVERAL MILLION POUNDS JUST TO CHANGE WHITE TO GREY ON THE COMPANY LOGO.

Panel 3: BUT WITH TIME ONE HAS COME RATHER TO APPRECIATE THE NEW COLOUR SCHEME. AN IMPRESSION REINFORCED WHEN ONE SUDDENLY CATCHES A GLIMPSE OF THE OLD LOGO...

Panel 4: ON THE FIRST CLASS LABEL ATTACHED TO A COLLEAGUE'S FLIGHT CASE.

OBVIOUSLY AN EMBARRASSINGLY LONG TIME SINCE HE LAST ENJOYED THE PRIVILEGE.